meeting Milly

written by Lucinda Cotter

illustrated by Donna Berger

"Mum, come quickly!" yelled Ned, as he opened the front door. "They're here!"

Dad had a big smile on his face. He was holding a small puppy. "Say hello to Milly," he said.

Ned couldn't believe it! Milly had arrived at last. Ned and his family were going to be "puppy raisers".

"She's very sweet," said Mum,
scratching Milly's ear.
"I wish we could keep
her longer than one year."

"I know," said Ned,
rubbing Milly under the chin.
"But Deb said that puppy raisers
can only have a puppy for one year.
Then the puppy must go away
and be trained as a guide dog."

Last year, Deb and her guide dog, Sultan,
had come to Ned's school.
Deb told the children that Sultan
went everywhere with her
and that Sultan was her special helper.

It was after Deb's visit that Ned
had the idea to be a puppy raiser.

On Milly's first night with the family,
Ned took Milly to her new bed
in the laundry.
"You're going to be
the best guide dog ever," said Ned,
patting her gently.
"We're going to take very good care
of you."

Milly gave a big yawn.
Then she rolled over
and quickly fell asleep.
It had been a big day.

The next morning,
when Mum and Dad were still asleep,
Ned went quietly downstairs
to check on Milly.
He opened the door and peeped inside.

"Mum! Dad!" cried Ned,
as he raced up the stairs.
"Milly is gone!
She's not in her bed."

"What do you mean, she's gone?"
asked Mum, rubbing her eyes.

"She's not in the laundry," said Ned.

"But how did she get out?"
asked Dad, scratching his head.
"The door was closed.
I shut it myself when I went to bed."

"Maybe she's been dog-napped!"
said Ned, looking worried.

Mum and Dad smiled.
"I don't think so," said Mum.
"She must be in the house somewhere."

"We just have to look for her," said Dad.

11

Ned, Mum and Dad looked
all over the house for Milly.

Ned looked under the beds
and behind the sofa.

Mum checked in the kitchen
and Dad even looked in the bath.
But Milly was nowhere to be found.

"I'm getting worried," said Ned.
"What if Milly is **really** lost?"

YiP! YiP! YiP!

"What was that?" asked Ned.
"It sounded just like a puppy."

"And," said Dad, scratching his head again,
"the sound is coming from the laundry."

Ned raced to the laundry,
but he couldn't **see** Milly.
He could only **hear** her!

YiP! YiP! YiP!

The puppy sound was coming
from inside the cupboard.

"Milly!" said Ned,
peeking inside the cupboard.
"What are you doing in here?"

YIP! YIP! YIP!

Inside the cupboard, behind a mop
and a bucket, was an old basket.
And there, sitting on top
of some old towels, was Milly.

15

Ned gently picked up the basket
and took it out of the cupboard.
Milly jumped up and licked Ned
on the cheek.

"Well," laughed Dad,
"it looks as if Milly has found
her own special bed."

"Yes," smiled Ned,
"a special bed for a **very** special puppy."